BABY'S TREASURED MEMORIES

A RECORD FROM BIRTH THROUGH SEVEN YEARS

Designed by Helen Lewis
Illustrated by Bonnie Finneran

Copyright 1995 E. L. Lewis, Inc., Carrollton, Ohio
Printed in USA

BABY'S TREASURED MEMORIES

Table of Contents

BABY'S ARRIVAL

It's a _____.
(boy or girl)

Born on_____,
(day of the week)

the _____ of
(date)

_____, _____,
(month)   *(year)*

at _____ _____. M.
(time)

Place of Birth_____

City/State_____

Country_____

Attending Physician_____

Nurse_____

NOTES

_____

_____

_____

FIRST PHOTOGRAPH

*photo
here*

Baby is named_____

Reason this name was chosen_____

_____ Date _____

BABY'S HOMECOMING

Baby arrives home on _____.
(date)

*photo
here*

Address _____

_____

*photo
of
parents
here*

BABY'S FOOTPRINTS

Date _____

BABY'S FAMILY

Notes about baby's family members, including sisters, brothers, aunts, uncles, cousins, or others:

_____

_____

_____

_____

_____

_____

_____

_____

_____

_____

_____

_____

_____

_____

_____

_____

FAMILY TREE

_____ Great Grandfather

_____ Great Grandmother

_____ Grandmother

_____ Great Grandfather

_____ Great Grandmother

_____ Grandfather

_____ Mother

_____ Baby

_____ Father

_____ Grandmother

_____ Grandfather

_____ Great Grandmother

_____ Great Grandmother

_____ Great Grandfather

_____ Great Grandfather

SHARING THE HAPPY NEWS

Attach copy here of the birth announcement
mailed to family and friends.

Attach here clippings from any other sources.
(Newsletters, Newspapers, Church Bulletin, etc.)

NEWS OF THE DAY

World & local top news stories:

_____

_____

_____

_____

_____

Major government officials:

_____

_____

_____

Popular songs, styles and entertainers:

_____

_____

_____

_____

BIRTH CERTIFICATE

*Please attach copy of
Birth Certificate
here.*

CEREMONIES AND CELEBRATIONS

Notes about baby's christening, Brith Milah, baptism, dedication, naming ceremony or other religious celebration or ceremony:

SHOWERS OF GIFTS AND GREETINGS
TO WELCOME BABY

BIRTH STATS

At birth, baby weighed _____ lbs. _____ ozs.

and was _____ inches in length.

Other measurements:

Head _____ inches

Chest _____ inches

Abdomen _____ inches

Eye color _____

Hair color _____

Other notes on first health examination after birth:

_____

_____

_____

_____

_____

_____

RECORD OF DOCTOR VISITS

Name of pediatrician or family practice physician: _____

Physician's office address: _____

Office hours phone: _____ After hours phone: _____

_____

_____

_____

_____

_____

_____

_____

_____

_____

_____

_____

_____

_____

_____

_____

_____

HEIGHT RECORD

1 week	_____	6 months	_____
2 weeks	_____	7 months	_____
3 weeks	_____	8 months	_____
1 month	_____	9 months	_____
5 weeks	_____	10 months	_____
6 weeks	_____	11 months	_____
7 weeks	_____	1 year	_____
2 months	_____	18 months	_____
9 weeks	_____	2 years	_____
10 weeks	_____	3 years	_____
11 weeks	_____	4 years	_____
3 months	_____	5 years	_____
4 months	_____	6 years	_____
5 months	_____	7 years	_____

WEIGHT RECORD

1 week	_____	6 months	_____
2 weeks	_____	7 months	_____
3 weeks	_____	8 months	_____
1 month	_____	9 months	_____
5 weeks	_____	10 months	_____
6 weeks	_____	11 months	_____
7 weeks	_____	1 year	_____
2 months	_____	18 months	_____
9 weeks	_____	2 years	_____
10 weeks	_____	3 years	_____
11 weeks	_____	4 years	_____
3 months	_____	5 years	_____
4 months	_____	6 years	_____
5 months	_____	7 years	_____

IMMUNIZATION RECORD

Please check with your child's physician or your state health department for specific recommendations on types of vaccinations and tests and the ages at which they should be administered. Use this space to accurately record all immunizations:

Immunization   Date Received

_____   _____

_____   _____

_____   _____

_____   _____

_____   _____

_____   _____

_____   _____

_____   _____

_____   _____

_____   _____

_____   _____

HOSPITAL VISITS

Notes on mishaps, accidents or illnesses requiring emergency-room care, surgery or hospitalization:

_____

_____

_____

_____

_____

_____

_____

RECORD OF ILLNESSES

Notes on childhood illnesses including dates, severity and any special circumstances:

_____

_____

_____

_____

_____

_____

BABY TEETH

First tooth appears _____
(date)

Approximate Dates Of Tooth Eruption

Upper	left	right		Lower	left	right
1	_____	_____		1	_____	_____
2	_____	_____		2	_____	_____
3	_____	_____		3	_____	_____
4	_____	_____		4	_____	_____
5	_____	_____		5	_____	_____

Notes about baby's teething:_____

_____

_____

Loses first baby tooth _____
(date)

Notes about loss of baby teeth to make room for permanent teeth: _____

_____

_____

RECORD OF DENTAL VISITS

Name of pediatric or family dentist: _____

Dental office address: _____

Office hours phone: _____ After hours phone: _____

EARLY DEVELOPMENTAL MILESTONES

Knows mother, father, etc. _____

Discovers own hands and feet _____

Reaches toward people or things _____

Picks up objects _____

Raises own head _____

Makes little sounds and "coos" _____

Laughs _____

Sleeps through the night _____

Rolls over _____

Crawls _____

Sits up alone _____

Aware of strangers _____

Pulls self up _____

Stands alone _____

Climbs stairs _____

Takes first steps _____

Walks alone _____

Holds bottle _____

Holds spoon and attempts feeding self _____

Holds cup alone and takes sips _____

Assists in dressing self _____

AT AGE ONE MONTH . . .

Length _____   Weight _____

Notes on appearance _____

Typical daily schedule _____

_____

Achievements _____

_____

Activities and experiences _____

_____

Favorites _____

_____

AT AGE TWO MONTHS . . .

Length _____   Weight _____

Changes in appearance _____

Typical daily schedule _____

_____

Achievements _____

_____

Activities and experiences _____

_____

Favorites _____

_____

AT AGE THREE MONTHS . . .

Length _____   Weight _____

Changes in appearance _____

Typical daily schedule _____

_____

Achievements _____

_____

Activities and experiences _____

_____

Favorites _____

_____

AT AGE FOUR MONTHS . . .

Length _____   Weight _____

Changes in appearance _____

Typical daily schedule _____

_____

Achievements _____

_____

Activities and experiences _____

_____

Favorites _____

_____

AT AGE FIVE MONTHS . . .

Length _____   Weight _____

Changes in appearance _____

Typical daily schedule _____

_____

Achievements _____

_____

Activities and experiences _____

_____

Favorites _____

_____

AT AGE SIX MONTHS . . .

Length _____   Weight _____

Changes in appearance _____

Typical daily schedule _____

_____

Achievements _____

_____

Activities and experiences _____

_____

Favorites _____

_____

AT AGE SEVEN MONTHS . . .

Length _____   Weight _____

Changes in appearance _____

Typical daily schedule _____

_____

Achievements _____

_____

Activities and experiences _____

_____

Favorites _____

_____

AT AGE EIGHT MONTHS . . .

Length _____   Weight _____

Changes in appearance _____

Typical daily schedule _____

_____

Achievements _____

_____

Activities and experiences _____

_____

Favorites _____

_____

AT AGE NINE MONTHS . . .

Length _____   Weight _____

Changes in appearance _____

Typical daily schedule _____

_____

Achievements _____

_____

Activities and experiences _____

_____

Favorites _____

_____

AT AGE TEN MONTHS . . .

Length _____   Weight _____

Changes in appearance _____

Typical daily schedule _____

_____

Achievements _____

_____

Activities and experiences _____

_____

Favorites _____

_____

AT AGE ELEVEN MONTHS . . .

Length ———————————— Weight ————————————

Changes in appearance —————————————————————

Typical daily schedule —————————————————————

————————————————————————————————

Achievements ————————————————————————

————————————————————————————————

Activities and experiences ————————————————————

————————————————————————————————

Favorites ——————————————————————————

————————————————————————————————

AT AGE ONE YEAR . . .

Length ———————————— Weight ————————————

Changes in appearance —————————————————————

Typical daily schedule —————————————————————

————————————————————————————————

Achievements ————————————————————————

————————————————————————————————

Activities and experiences ————————————————————

————————————————————————————————

Favorites ——————————————————————————

————————————————————————————————

AT AGE EIGHTEEN MONTHS . . .

Height _____   Weight _____

Changes in appearance _____

Typical daily schedule _____

_____

Achievements _____

_____

Activities and experiences _____

_____

Favorites _____

_____

AT AGE TWO YEARS . . .

Height _____   Weight _____

Changes in appearance _____

Typical daily schedule _____

_____

Achievements _____

_____

Activities and experiences _____

_____

Favorites _____

_____

AT AGE THREE YEARS . . .

Height _____   Weight _____

Changes in appearance _____

Typical daily schedule _____

_____

Achievements and talents _____

_____

Activities and experiences _____

_____

Favorites _____

_____

AT AGE FOUR YEARS . . .

Height _____   Weight _____

Changes in appearance _____

Typical daily schedule _____

_____

Achievements and talents _____

_____

Activities and experiences _____

_____

Favorites _____

_____

AT AGE FIVE YEARS . . .

Height ———————————— Weight ————————————

Changes in appearance ————————————————————

Typical daily schedule ————————————————————

————————————————————————————————————

Achievements and talents ——————————————————

————————————————————————————————————

Activities and experiences —————————————————

————————————————————————————————————

Favorites ———————————————————————————

————————————————————————————————————

AT AGE SIX YEARS . . .

Height ———————————— Weight ————————————

Changes in appearance ————————————————————

Typical daily schedule ————————————————————

————————————————————————————————————

Achievements and talents ——————————————————

————————————————————————————————————

Activities and experiences —————————————————

————————————————————————————————————

Favorites ———————————————————————————

————————————————————————————————————

AT AGE SEVEN YEARS . . .

Height _____   Weight _____

Changes in appearance _____

Typical daily schedule _____

_____

Achievements and talents _____

_____

Activities and experiences _____

_____

Favorites _____

_____

OTHER EARLY DEVELOPMENTAL NOTES

_____

_____

_____

_____

_____

_____

LANGUAGE AND VERBAL DEVELOPMENT

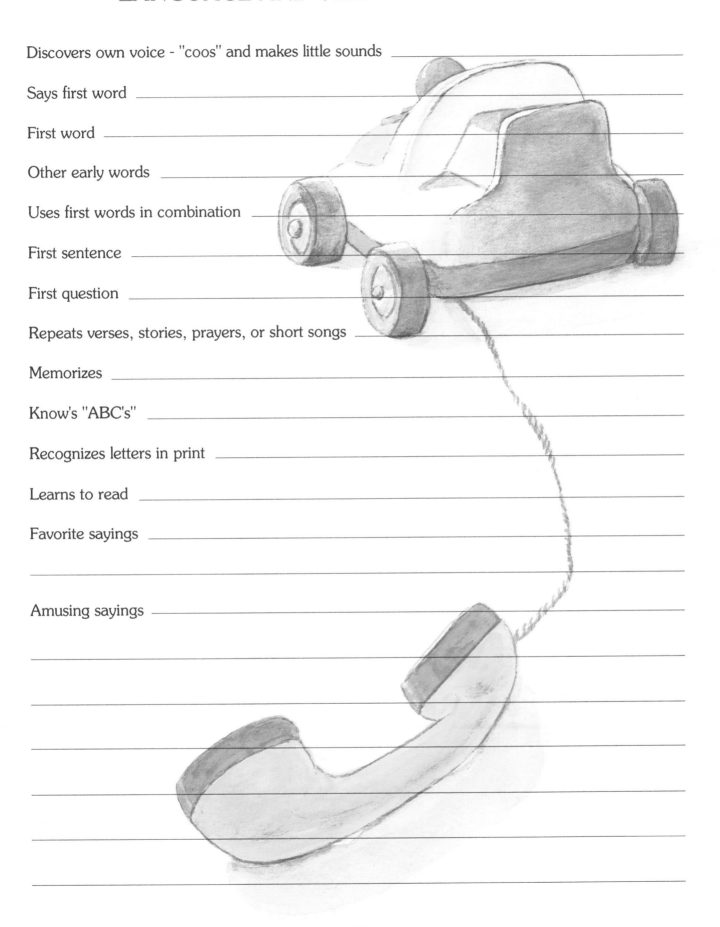

Discovers own voice - "coos" and makes little sounds _____

Says first word _____

First word _____

Other early words _____

Uses first words in combination _____

First sentence _____

First question _____

Repeats verses, stories, prayers, or short songs _____

Memorizes _____

Know's "ABC's" _____

Recognizes letters in print _____

Learns to read _____

Favorite sayings _____

_____

Amusing sayings _____

_____

_____

_____

_____

_____

FIRST HAIRCUT

Date _____ Haircut given by _____

Notes _____

_____

"before"
photo

"after"
photo

FIRST FRIENDSHIPS

_____

_____

_____

_____

_____

_____

_____

_____

_____

_____

_____

FIRST PETS

_____

_____

_____

_____

_____

_____

_____

PRESCHOOL

Name of school _____

Address of school _____

Dates of attendance _____

First teachers _____

Notes on favorite activities, friends, or highlights _____

_____

_____

_____

_____

_____

_____

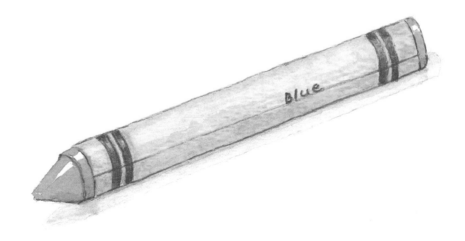

KINDERGARTEN

Name of school

Address of school

Dates of attendance

Teacher's name

Notes on favorite activities, friends, accomplishments or highlights

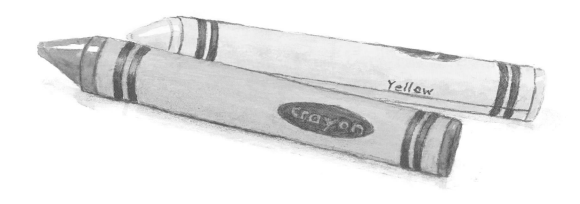

FIRST GRADE

Name of school _____

Address of school _____

Dates of attendance _____

Teacher's name _____

Notes on favorite activities, lessons, friends, accomplishments or highlights_____

_____

_____

_____

_____

_____

_____

RELIGIOUS EDUCATION

First Church, Synagogue or Mosque _____

Address _____

Clergymen's names _____

Teachers' names _____

_____

_____

Notes on favorite prayers, stories, songs or other religious activities:

_____

_____

_____

_____

_____

_____

_____

_____

_____

_____

_____

FIRST BIRTHDAY

Notes about the celebration _____

_____

_____

_____

_____

Family and friends who were there _____

_____

_____

_____

Major family or world events of the last year _____

_____

_____

Special birthday remembrances, presents, etc. _____

_____

_____

_____

_____

_____

_____

_____

_____

_____

SECOND BIRTHDAY

Notes about the celebration _____

_____

_____

_____

_____

Family and friends who were there _____

_____

_____

_____

Major family or world events of the last year _____

_____

_____

Special birthday remembrances, presents, etc. _____

_____

_____

_____

_____

_____

_____

_____

_____

THIRD BIRTHDAY

Notes about the celebration _____

_____

_____

_____

_____

Family and friends who were there _____

_____

_____

_____

_____

Major family or world events of the last year _____

_____

_____

Special birthday remembrances, presents, etc. _____

_____

_____

_____

_____

_____

_____

FOURTH BIRTHDAY

Notes about the celebration _____

_____

_____

_____

_____

Family and friends who were there _____

_____

_____

_____

_____

Major family or world events of the last year _____

_____

_____

Special birthday remembrances, presents, etc. _____

_____

_____

_____

_____

_____

_____

_____

FIFTH BIRTHDAY

Notes about the celebration _____

_____

_____

_____

_____

Family and friends who were there _____

_____

_____

_____

Major family or world events of the last year _____

_____

_____

Special birthday remembrances, presents, etc. _____

_____

_____

_____

_____

_____

_____

_____

_____

_____

SIXTH BIRTHDAY

Notes about the celebration _____

_____

_____

_____

_____

Family and friends who were there _____

_____

_____

_____

Major family or world events of the last year _____

_____

_____

Special birthday remembrances, presents, etc. _____

_____

_____

_____

_____

_____

_____

_____

SEVENTH BIRTHDAY

Notes about the celebration _____

_____

_____

_____

_____

Family and friends who were there _____

_____

_____

_____

_____

Major family or world events of the last year _____

_____

_____

Special birthday remembrances, presents, etc. _____

_____

_____

_____

_____

_____

_____

_____

_____

TRIPS AND VACATIONS

Date _____ Destination _____

Notes _____

_____

Date _____ Destination _____

Notes _____

_____

Date _____ Destination _____

Notes _____

_____

Date _____ Destination _____

Notes _____

_____

Date _____ Destination _____

Notes _____

_____

Date _____ Destination _____

Notes _____

_____

Date _____ Destination _____

Notes _____

_____

OUTSIDE ACTIVITIES

Music, dance or other lessons _____

_____

_____

Dates _____ Teachers _____

Notes _____

_____

_____

Lessons in sports or first team sport _____

_____

_____

Dates _____ Instructors or Coaches _____

Notes _____

_____

_____

Other favorite activities or aptitudes _____

_____

_____

_____

_____

SPECIAL REMEMBRANCES

Notes on any funny or outstanding incidents, actions or comments:

HOLIDAY CELEBRATIONS

Notes on special holidays including dates and how they were celebrated:

HOLIDAY CELEBRATIONS

More notes on holidays including dates and how they were celebrated: